# SELECTIONS

### FOR VIOLIN AND PIANO
### FROM

# Porgy & Bess

### TRANSCRIBED BY
## JASCHA HEIFETZ

© 2007 by Faber Music Ltd
First published by International Music Publications Ltd
International Music Publications Ltd is a Faber Music company
Bloomsbury House, 74–77 Great Russell Street, London WC1B 3DA
Printed in England by Caligraving Ltd
All rights reserved

ISBN10: 0-571-53085-0
EAN13: 978-0-571-53085-4

To buy Faber Music publications or to find out about the full range of titles available,
please contact your local music retailer or Faber Music sales enquiries:

Faber Music Ltd, Burnt Mill, Elizabeth Way, Harlow, CM20 2HX England
Tel: +44(0)1279 82 89 82
fabermusic.com

# "Summertime" and
# "A Woman is a Sometime Thing"

By George Gershwin, Dubose and
Dorothy Heyward and Ira Gershwin
Transcribed by Heifetz

Con Moto (♩. = 96)

# It Ain't Necessarily So

By George Gershwin, Dubose and
Dorothy Heyward and Ira Gershwin
Transcribed by Heifetz

FOR VIOLIN AND PIANO
FROM

VIOLIN PART

TRANSCRIBED BY

# JASCHA HEIFETZ

© 2007 by Faber Music Ltd
First published by International Music Publications Ltd
International Music Publications Ltd is a Faber Music company
Bloomsbury House, 74–77 Great Russell Street, London WC1B 3DA
Printed in England by Caligraving Ltd
All rights reserved

ISBN10: 0-571-53085-0
EAN13: 978-0-571-53085-4

To buy Faber Music publications or to find out about the full range of titles available,
please contact your local music retailer or Faber Music sales enquiries:

Faber Music Ltd, Burnt Mill, Elizabeth Way, Harlow, CM20 2HX England
Tel: +44(0)1279 82 89 82
fabermusic.com

# "Summertime" and
# "A Woman is a Sometime Thing"

**Violin**

By George Gershwin, Dubose and
Dorothy Heyward and Ira Gershwin
Transcribed by Heifetz

## Violin

# It Ain't Necessarily So

By George Gershwin, Dubose and
Dorothy Heyward and Ira Gershwin
Transcribed by Heifetz

Violin

# Violin

* Approx. to B♮ - without reaching any *particular* note.

# Bess, You Is My Woman Now

Violin

By George Gershwin, Dubose and
Dorothy Heyward and Ira Gershwin
Transcribed by Heifetz

A cut may be made from this sign to the next asterik

*Approx. to B♮ - without reaching any *particular* note.

# Bess, You Is My Woman Now

By George Gershwin, Dubose and
Dorothy Heyward and Ira Gershwin
Transcribed by Heifetz

*A cut may be made from this sign to the next asterik

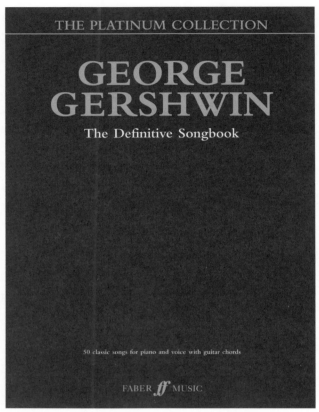

THE PLATINUM COLLECTION

# GEORGE GERSHWIN

The Definitive Songbook

50 classic songs for piano and voice with guitar chords

FABER ff MUSIC

ISBN10: 0-571-52684-5
EAN13: 978-0-571-52684-0

The definitive Gershwin songbook, featuring 50 of George Gershwin's best songs for piano and voice with guitar chords.

A Foggy Day · Bess, You Is My Woman · Bidin' My Time · But Not For Me
By Strauss · Clap Yo' Hands · Do It Again · Do, Do, Do
Embraceable You · Fascinating Rhythm · Fidgety Feet · Funny Face
He Loves And She Loves · High Hat · How Long Has This Been Going On? · I Got Plenty O' Nuttin'
I Got Rhythm · I'll Build A Stairway To Paradise · I've Got A Crush On You · Isn't It A Pity?
It Ain't Necessarily So · Let's Call The Whole Thing Off · Let's Kiss And Make Up · Love Is Here To Stay
Love Is Sweeping The Country · Love Walked In · Maybe · Mine
My One And Only · Nice Work If You Can Get It · Of Thee I Sing · Oh, Kay!
Oh, Lady, Be Good! · Rosalie · Slap That Bass · Somebody Loves Me
Someone To Watch Over Me · Strike Up The Band · Summertime · Swanee
'S Wonderful · Sweet And Low-Down · That Certain Feeling · The Babbitt And The Bromide
The Half Of It, Dearie Blues · The Man I Love · They All Laughed
They Can't Take That Away From Me · Things Are Looking Up · Who Cares?

To buy Faber Music publications or to find out about the full range of titles available
please contact your local music retailer or Faber Music sales enquiries:

Faber Music Ltd, Burnt Mill, Elizabeth Way, Harlow CM20 2HX
Tel: +44 (0) 1279 82 89 82
fabermusic.com